Come to Me!

The Story of Jesus and the Children

Any questions or comments about *God Loves Me?* We'd love to hear from you.

Faith Alive Christian Resources
1-800-333-8300
editors@faithaliveresources.org

We are grateful to early childhood educators Jesslyn DeBoer, Patricia Nederveld, Sherry Ten Clay, and Yvonne Van Ee for their contributions to *God Loves Me*, a Bible story program for young children. We are also grateful to Estudio Haus for illustrating this children's book.

Photos on pages 5 and 20: iStockphoto.

ISBN 978-1-59255-868-1

10 9 8 7 6 5 4 3 2 1

Come to Me!

The Story of Jesus and the Children

PATRICIA L. NEDERVELD

ILLUSTRATIONS BY ESTUDIO HAUS

FAITH
ALIVE®
Christian Resources

Grand Rapids, Michigan

This is a story from
God's book, the Bible.

It's for say name(s) of your child(ren).
It's for me too!

Mark 10:13-16

Moms who love Jesus want their children to love Jesus too. Dads who love Jesus know that Jesus loves boys and girls very much!

Long ago, when Jesus lived on earth, some moms and dads took their boys and girls to see him. "Maybe Jesus will hug our children and tell them stories. What a wonderful time that would be!" they thought.

They did find Jesus! But he was very busy teaching grown-ups. The moms and dads and boys and girls waited. Would Jesus be happy to see them? Would he have time to talk to children too?

Jesus' helpers thought Jesus
was far too busy to play
with children. "Go away!
Don't bother Jesus today.
He's busy!"
they said.

But Jesus didn't feel too busy. "Don't tell the children to go away! I want them to come to me. Don't you know that boys and girls are an important part of God's family?" Then Jesus smiled at the children.

The boys and girls smiled back at Jesus. They climbed onto his lap. They listened to his stories. They could tell that Jesus loved them. Everyone had a wonderful time—especially Jesus!

That day everyone knew that Jesus loves children. Jesus' helpers knew. The moms knew. The dads knew too. And best of all, each little girl and each little boy knew that Jesus loves children very much!

I wonder if you know that Jesus loves you very much . . .

Dear Jesus, thank you for loving moms and dads, boys and girls, and babies too. We love you, Jesus. Amen.

Suggestions for Using This Book

In a Group Setting
Opening and Story Time

Welcome the children and tell them you have some great news for them—but you want to whisper it in their ears. Invite each child to come and sit in your lap as you whisper, "Jesus loves you very much, [name]!" Pass around this storybook so everyone can see its cover picture of Jesus with the children gathered around him. You might want to tell the group it's one of your favorite stories about Jesus.

Read this book to the children, beginning on page 4 and inserting their names. Make sure everyone can see the pictures and go slowly, giving the children time to point to things that capture their imaginations or to respond to the story. You'll want to encourage everyone to respond to the question on page 21 too. End your story with the prayer printed there.

Learning Through Play

The suggestions listed here are meant to help you provide props and experiences that will invite your twos and threes to play their way into the Scripture story and its simple truth. Try to provide plenty of time for the children to choose their own activities and to explore and play individually, which is the way of young children! Use group activities sparingly—little ones learn most comfortably (and happily) with a minimum of structure.

- In your art area, provide glue sticks, a picture of Jesus (*God Loves Me* pattern 18), and lots of pictures of children cut from magazines and catalogs. In the center of a large sheet of posterboard glue the picture of Jesus and write below it: JESUS LOVES CHILDREN! Read the caption aloud and ask the group to shout out the words three or four times with you. Then invite them to fill up all the empty space around Jesus with pictures of kids—big kids, little kids, and babies.

- If you have older children in your group, they may enjoy drawing pictures of themselves (to which you can add the caption: JESUS LOVES ME!). Or, you could provide child shaped cutouts (*God Loves Me* pattern 9) for the children to fill in with color and to glue to a background. Add the above caption to each completed picture.

- Encourage lots of pretending in your housekeeping area. Make sure there are plenty of dolls available and suggest the kids pretend to be mommies or daddies today. Talk about how much Jesus loves mommies and daddies—and how glad Jesus was that mommies and daddies brought their children and babies to see him. It was easy to see how much Jesus loved those kids.

- Here are some possibilities for music time: "God Made Me, Every Part You See" (*Sing with Me Preschool Songs*, track 4), "Jesus Loves Me" (track 16), "Jesus, I Love You" (track 17), and "Thank You, Jesus" (track 18). Use each selection as another opportunity to remind the children how much Jesus loves them.

- If your children enjoy games, here's one you might try together. Gather the children around you and tell them you are thinking about someone—someone Jesus loves very much. Tell them you will help them guess who that someone is. Then describe one of the children in your group. Ask the children to look all around and find the child you're thinking of. When they do, everybody gets to say: "Jesus loves you, [name]!"

- Use your snack time to talk about other children Jesus loves. If you have a church directory that pictures church members, page through it and let the children find other kids Jesus loves. Talk about the brothers and sisters of the children in your group too—Jesus also loves them very much!

Closing

Call the children back together a few minutes before the end of their playtime; using a bell or music or a special rhyme works well. Make a circle, join hands, and close with a short prayer thanking Jesus for loving each child in your group (mention each one by name)—or repeat the prayer on page 21.

At Home

Home is the first place little ones learn how much they are loved by Jesus. Here's a game you might play with your child this week. Ask him or her, "Guess who loves you very much?" Answer with the name of a friend or family member; then repeat the question, each time adding a new name. End by adding Jesus' name to the list and saying, "And that's the best news of all!"

Old Testament Stories

1 **Blue and Green and Purple Too!** *The Story of God's Colorful World*

2 **It's a Noisy Place!** *The Story of the First Creatures*

3 **Adam and Eve** *The Story of the First Man and Woman*

4 **Take Good Care of My World!** *The Story of Adam and Eve in the Garden*

5 **A Very Sad Day** *The Story of Adam and Eve's Disobedience*

6 **A Rainy, Rainy Day** *The Story of Noah*

7 **Count the Stars!** *The Story of God's Promise to Abraham and Sarah*

8 **A Girl Named Rebekah** *The Story of God's Answer to Abraham*

9 **Two Coats for Joseph** *The Story of Young Joseph*

10 **Plenty to Eat** *The Story of Joseph and His Brothers*

11 **Safe in a Basket** *The Story of Baby Moses*

12 **I'll Do It!** *The Story of Moses and the Burning Bush*

13 **Safe at Last!** *The Story of Moses and the Red Sea*

14 **What Is It?** *The Story of Manna in the Desert*

15 **A Tall Wall** *The Story of Jericho*

16 **A Baby for Hannah** *The Story of an Answered Prayer*

17 **Samuel, Samuel!** *The Story of God's Call to Samuel*

18 **Lions and Bears!** *The Story of David the Shepherd Boy*

19 **David and the Giant** *The Story of David and Goliath*

20 **A Little Jar of Oil** *The Story of Elisha and the Widow*

21 **One, Two, Three, Four, Five, Six, Seven!** *The Story of Elisha and Naaman*

22 **A Big Fish Story** *The Story of Jonah*

23 **Lions, Lions!** *The Story of Daniel*

New Testament Stories

24 **Jesus Is Born!** *The Story of Christmas*

25 **Good News!** *The Story of the Shepherds*

26 **An Amazing Star!** *The Story of the Wise Men*

27 **Waiting, Waiting, Waiting!** *The Story of Simeon and Anna*

28 **Who Is This Child?** *The Story of Jesus in the Temple*

29 **Follow Me!** *The Story of Jesus and His Twelve Helpers*

30 **The Greatest Gift** *The Story of Jesus and the Woman at the Well*

31 **A Father's Wish** *The Story of Jesus and a Little Boy*

32 **Just Believe!** *The Story of Jesus and a Little Girl*

33 **Get Up and Walk!** *The Story of Jesus and a Man Who Couldn't Walk*

34 **A Little Lunch** *The Story of Jesus and a Hungry Crowd*

35 **A Scary Storm** *The Story of Jesus and a Stormy Sea*

36 **Thank You, Jesus!** *The Story of Jesus and One Thankful Man*

37 **A Wonderful Sight!** *The Story of Jesus and a Man Who Couldn't See*

38 **A Better Thing to Do** *The Story of Jesus and Mary and Martha*

39 **A Lost Lamb** *The Story of the Good Shepherd*

40 **Come to Me!** *The Story of Jesus and the Children*

41 **Have a Great Day!** *The Story of Jesus and Zacchaeus*

42 **I Love You, Jesus!** *The Story of Mary's Gift to Jesus*

43 **Hosanna!** *The Story of Palm Sunday*

44 **The Best Day Ever!** *The Story of Easter*

45 **Goodbye—for Now** *The Story of Jesus' Return to Heaven*

46 **A Prayer for Peter** *The Story of Peter in Prison*

47 **Sad Day, Happy Day!** *The Story of Peter and Dorcas*

48 **A New Friend** *The Story of Paul's Conversion*

49 **Over the Wall** *The Story of Paul's Escape in a Basket*

50 **A Song in the Night** *The Story of Paul and Silas in Prison*

51 **A Ride in the Night** *The Story of Paul's Escape on Horseback*

52 **The Shipwreck** *The Story of Paul's Rescue at Sea*

Holiday Stories

Selected stories from the New Testament to help you celebrate the Christian year

24 **Jesus Is Born!** *The Story of Christmas*

25 **Good News!** *The Story of the Shepherds*

26 **An Amazing Star!** *The Story of the Wise Men*

43 **Hosanna!** *The Story of Palm Sunday*

44 **The Best Day Ever!** *The Story of Easter*

45 **Goodbye—for Now** *The Story of Jesus' Return to Heaven*

These fifty-two books are the heart of *God Loves Me*, a Bible story program designed for young children. Individual books (or the entire set) and the accompanying program guide can be ordered from Faith Alive Christian Resources at *www.faithaliveresources.org* or by calling 1-800-333-8300.